WHAT I WISH
I KNEW BACK
THEN

*A Physical Therapist and
Mother's Perspective of Raising
Her Child with Cerebral Palsy*

Marsh Naidoo, PT

Raising Kellan, Inc.

ISBN ebook: 978-1-7352240-0-8
ISBN paperback: 978-1-7352240-1-5

For All Our Cerebral Palsy Warriors

CONTENTS

WHAT I WISH I KNEW BACK THEN

Author:
Marsh Naidoo, PT

Contributing Authors:
Dana Kramer
Lauren Taylor
and
Aspen Balthazor, DPT

Illustrator: Hope Khalil

Editor: Terra Temple

WHAT IS RAISING KELLAN, INC.?

R aising Kellan, Inc. is a nonprofit organization and a digital platform that consists of the Raising Kellan Blog and Podcast, both found at www.raisingkellan.org.

OUR MISSION STATEMENT: The goal of Raising Kellan, Inc. is to create a community focused on reducing the parental anxiety that comes from facing the unknown of raising a child with a developmental delay or disability.

OUR PURPOSE: Raising Kellan, Inc. will provide support to parents and guardians of children with disabilities so they remain empowered, educated and equipped to help their children reach their optimal level of function and ability. The corporation is organized for the charitable and educational purposes of providing parents and guardians of children with disabilities, as well as individuals with disabilities, support and skills to reach their full potential and to become contributing members of their communities.

OUR VISION STATEMENT: To create a movement that challenges how the world views our children and how our children view the world.

The sale of this book and future books will be used to sustain the mission and vision of this community-based organization. We thank you for your support, and we look forward to hearing from you at raisingkellan@gmail.com.

"Always get to the top of your mountain."

Preface

I am a physical therapist, or a physiotherapist as we are known in some parts of the world. I graduated from the University of KwaZulu-Natal in South Africa.

My passion for travel has taken me to Europe, Asia and the United States of America, where I lived and worked as a physical therapist for over a decade.

In 2008, I met Prakash while visiting my parents in South Africa. We married in 2009 and decided to make our home in South Africa.

But life had other plans.

Kellan came along!

Introduction

I was not prepared for the birth of my son Kellan at 26 weeks ... or for what followed. Managing Kellan's cerebral palsy and moving him towards independence is a roller coaster ride. Most of the time it leaves me overwhelmed, vulnerable and second-guessing myself: "Am I doing enough? Am I doing the right thing? Is this going to work?"

Even with my academic background and 24 years of experience as a physical therapist, raising my son Kellan is daunting. It is literally like having a blueprint, but struggling to fit the pieces of the puzzle together. In those early years, I remember sifting through the internet desperately trying to find resources and wanting to connect with parents who had insight in raising a child with a developmental delay or a disability. Surprisingly, it wasn't just the current medical research I scrambled after; what I needed to see were real-life examples of parents raising their children with developmental challenges. I wanted guidelines on how to navigate my life with my child, but relevant and practical information was hard to come by.

We are now eight years into our journey. The passage of time has given me insight with the hands-on experience of raising Kellan. As I reflect back to those early years, I feel the responsibility to pass on my experiences, first as a mother and secondly as a physical therapist. I am not an expert or an authority by any means. I am just a mom who is traveling this road.

My intent is to specifically help that parent who is leaving the doctor's office with their baby having received this diagnosis of developmental delay — their world is shattered, they are panic-stricken, they are trying to figure out "How am I going to do this? How am I going to help my child? What is life going to be like for my child?"

It is my mission to reduce some of the fear and anxiety that comes from facing the unknown when raising your child who has a developmental delay. My vision is for us to create a movement that challenges how the world views our children and how our children view the world.

I created the Raising Kellan Blog and Podcast as a platform to motivate, inspire and educate parents in the challenges that lie ahead to better serve their child. I am grateful to our community of guest bloggers, namely Dana Kramer, Lauren Taylor and Aspen Balthazor, DPT who have agreed to share their diverse experiences in this book.

If you are reading this book as a parent faced with a recent diagnosis of developmental delay, I

want you to first know you are not alone. Secondly, this book was created for you by parents just like you. As you read these pages, I hope you find comfort, connection and community.

The narrative in this book is simply informational. Its purpose is to provide practical knowledge and share the value of our collective experiences. The scope of this book does not provide medical advice and, as always, you should consult your healthcare provider for your child's medical needs.

"Start by doing what's necessary;
Then do what's possible;
And then suddenly you are doing the impossible."
— Saint Francis of Assisi

What Is Cerebral Palsy?

C erebral palsy (CP) is reported to be the most common childhood disability. Each child with cerebral palsy is affected differently, according to the area of the brain that is injured. This interruption of brain growth can occur intrauterine, during the birthing process or up to the age of 2. It results in changes of postural control, muscle tone, movement patterns, balance, coordination and sensory integration and regulation.

The umbrella term of developmental delay is referred to when anticipated childhood milestones are not met. Developmental delay is considered a symptom of several diagnoses including autism, cerebral palsy, muscular dystrophies and genetic conditions such as Down Syndrome. Cerebral palsy is a complex medical condition with a global delay in physical, speech and cognitive developments. This global delay is not surprising as a child needs to stack and master skills in sequence to unlock the next milestone or developmental level.

It is important to clarify that not all developmental delays evolve into disability. The Americans with Disabilities Act defines disability as a physical or mental impairment that substantially limits an individual in one or more major life activities.

As devastating as the initial diagnosis of developmental delay is, there is good news. Early intervention (EI) is an essential service that provides children between birth to 3-years old and their families with support services such as physical, occupational and speech therapies (PT/OT/ST) to teach the child physical skills (reaching, rolling, sitting, crawling, walking), social and emotional skills (playing, sharing), communication (listening, talking, understanding), cognitive skills (learning, problem solving, memory) and self-care skills (feeding, dressing, toileting). Early intervention services improve future outcomes and quality of life for a child with developmental delay. These services are state-funded in the United States.

It is prudent to provide opportunities for a child to learn skills as early as possible. In the pediatric population, I have seen how therapists work together to promote the child's ability to move and transition between positions, for example: from laying down, rolling to their side and then using their arms to push up into sitting, or sitting and pulling into standing. During early intervention, therapists use play and other techniques to strategically create an environment for learning; it's the repetition and practice that leads to the movement being mastered.

The stigma historically associated with disabilities appears to be down trending. The perception of cerebral palsy is changing with parental advocacy, educational awareness boosted by technology, growing media representation and individuals with cerebral palsy making a positive impact on their communities and the world at large. Let's have more of this, and with momentum of this scale, inclusion is truly possible.

"Be the change that you wish to see in the world."

— Mahatma Gandhi

What I Wish I Knew
Back Then ...

T his book is a recollection of my experiences during Kellan's early years and traces the journey from his birth in Durban, South Africa, to his cerebral palsy diagnosis. I structured my narrative to feature the significant challenges I encountered along the way. As you navigate these modes of survival, uncertainty and call-to-action, you will learn some of the strategies I wielded to cope and how I adapted my mindset to accept the unexpected and thrive.

Survival Mode

Kellan's entry into this world was dramatic, to say the least. I went into premature labor at 24 weeks and was hospitalized for bed rest and medical management. Two weeks later, on June 21, 2012, my water broke. Kellan was delivered via C-section on what was our third wedding anniversary! He weighed 840 grams (1.8 pounds) and measured 35 centimeters (13.7 inches).

The overwhelming experience of his premature birth and the neonatal intensive care unit (NICU) was initially numbing. It catapulted me into a fight-and-flight frenzy. The fear and angst were indescribable. My only prayer was for my baby to survive.

I was transported to a completely different world when my baby was transferred to the NICU. The NICU has its own ebb and flow. The nurses calmly steered me toward the routine of taking care of Kellan. In retrospect, staying focused on his needs centered me. It forged our bond that was un-timely interrupted by his earlier-than-expected arrival and established my accountability for his care. This responsibility dispelled some of my anxiety and fear of losing him.

Each day brought the promise of hope as he slowly became more robust, breathing independently, regulating his heart rate and body temperature and learning how to suck and feed. Kellan's first milestone was reaching 1 kilogram (2.5 pounds). This was my affirmation that my baby was going to survive.

The compassion and skill of the NICU team guided Kellan to safety, and he graduated to come home on September 1, 2012. Carrying him through those hospital doors, I realized the miracle of his survival. I would later reflect on this defining moment and be awestruck by the enormity of God's grace and the profound purpose Kellan's life would give ours.

My takeaway from our three-month NICU stay was the importance of kangaroo care, or kangaroo mother care. This technique mimics marsupials, such as the kangaroo which carries the young joey inside her pouch where it also nurses. The practice of kangaroo care actually started in the 1970s in Bogata, Colombia, when due to the shortage of incubators, low birth weight infants were placed on their mother's chest for most of the day to keep the baby warm, regulate their heart and breathing rates and to encourage breastfeeding.

This skin-to-skin contact of Kellan on my or Prakash's chest promoted our parent-child connection, reduced the risk of infections and decreased stress levels by removing the artificial barrier of the incubator until he was ready to be weaned off it.

We had to prepare for Kellan's homecoming. Top on the list was a sleep apnea monitor. This device was used to track Kellan's breathing. In fact, his neonatologist refused to discharge him until I had one in hand. It was recommended that I position him on his tummy with his head turned to either side for short periods throughout the day and to continue to perform kangaroo care, which I instinctively coupled with gentle rocking, stroking and playing soothing background music. Kangaroo care is a form of neuroplasticity, and it would be several years later that I would come to understand the science of neuroplasticity and how providing a multisensory experience creates neural pathways in response to learning from the environment after brain injury.

We arrived home on September 1, 2012, and life settled into a natural rhythm.

Uncertainty Mode

When Kellan was 6-months old, alarm bells started going off. I was inspired to see him track with his eyes, follow sounds, smile; however, sporadic observations started to form a pattern. He was rolling from his tummy onto his back but not in the opposite direction. He was very low toned (jelly-like) in his trunk; he could not sit without support and he would startle frequently.

This startle reflex is one of a group of primitive reflexes needed during the birthing process and in the first few months of life. Other examples include the rooting reflex and palmar grasp. Their job is to basically protect the infant as they learn their new environment. When primitive reflexes are retained, they block voluntary and purposeful movements from developing. I also looked for spasticity, but this emerged later when he began to challenge himself by moving against gravity.

❈ ❈ ❈

What is Spasticity?

Spasticity is often described as muscle "stiffness" or "tightness," but the issue is not with the muscle.

Spasticity is a result of brain or spinal cord injury and it is referred to in scientific terms as an upper motor neuron lesion. Muscles with this increased tone are confused with being "strong," but this is not the case.

Spasticity can be classified according to its pattern of distribution. Spasticity that mostly occurs in the legs is referred to as spastic diplegia cerebral palsy; an arm and leg affected on the same side is called spastic hemiplegia cerebral palsy; three limbs affected is called spastic triplegia cerebral palsy; and if both arms and legs are involved, this is called spastic quadriplegia cerebral palsy.

Over time, spasticity can destroy muscles and joints forming contractures (a condition of shortening and hardening of muscles, tendons or other tissue, often leading to deformity and rigidity of joints), as well as impact the other systems of the body, including the heart, lungs, gastrointestinal tract and the skin.

* * *

Kellan not meeting those early milestones was explained away due to his prematurity. His pediatrician would not comment on questions along the lines of "Is he alright?" Even though my physical therapy instincts subconsciously kicked in, I spent much of that first year in limbo: balancing taking care of my first child and trying to figure out if this is how things should be.

I have often contemplated the rationale of why medical professionals are so reluctant to discuss the potential of developmental delay with parents. Yes, there are some children who "catch up"; and it may be deemed as unnecessary to "worry" the parents. But what about those children who don't "catch up"? In my opinion, playing this waiting game leads to wasted time and, in some cases, missed opportunity.

I am grateful Kellan was referred to a neurodevelopmental trained (NDT) physiotherapist (physical therapist) at a year old. An MRI at 14-months old confirmed his diagnosis of cerebral palsy.

My takeaway from this time period is to first "always trust your gut." Secondly, start early intervention (EI) services as soon as possible. I know that for parents the focus on receiving a definitive diagnosis is often touted as the be-all and end-all. I am not suggesting that the search for your child's diagnosis be put on hold. What I am saying is do not put early intervention on hold until you have a diagnosis. I believe early intervention is the key. In my opinion, this is the best chance of you helping your child's long-term prognosis and functional outcomes. The reality is that as they become older they become heavier, so those early years count.

* * *

What is Early Intervention?

Early intervention services refer to programs that provide physical, occupational and speech therapy (PT/OT/ST) services to infants from birth to 3-years old with developmental delays or disabilities. The referral to these services is most often made by your child's pediatrician; therefore, this conversation with your medical provider needs to happen sooner rather than later. I hope these open lines of communication with your doctor lead you to the referral of pediatric providers who are specifically equipped and trained to provide services to your child.

Make sure you research your child's medical and therapy providers as these individuals are potentially going to guide you and your child for a long time. Recommendations from multiple parents in your area may be helpful. Doing the work upfront and investing the energy in finding the right providers saves a lot of time and resources down the line.

❋ ❋ ❋

My Career as a Physical Therapist

As a physical therapist, I work with individuals who are ill or injured to get them back to what they were doing before or as close to it as possible. My practice before Kellan's birth was mostly orthopedic outpatient-based, treating adults with strains/sprains or fractures (broken bones) and patients who had become deconditioned after illness or surgery.

Because of my profession, I have a good understanding of the body and how it works, what happens to the body when there is a disruption of the biomechanics and how to help the body get into gear so you can optimally function in your life and community.

Before Kellan, my pediatric skills were limited to a six-week clinical rotation. Having the theory is one thing; having practical experience is something completely different. During Kellan's early years, I focused on nurturing him, providing a safe, loving environment and being his backup therapist. Fast forward to the present day, I would say I definitely have a better understanding of how to engage with my son on his level now that he is older and motivated to want to do more.

These practical skills I actually learned from the guidance of Kellan's pediatric therapists, who have been awesome mentors. Trust me when I say that any parent with a willingness to learn can become an expert on how to provide therapeutic opportunities for their child to move, talk and play. You are your child's best therapist by default since you spend more time with them.

I close my eyes and reflect back to when Kellan was 4-years old and how I would rock him to John Lennon's song "Beautiful Boy." I love that song, especially the lyrics "Life is what happens while you're busy making other plans." Sure, there is a focus on doing therapies, but take some time to make memories.

I often get asked if my skills as a physical therapist help with managing Kellan's cerebral palsy. My answer would be yes and no. Yes, it made my navigation of the medical system easier. No, working with kids (even if he's mine) takes a completely different treatment approach. I must admit it's sometimes difficult to switch off the therapist mode! Raising Kellan has made me an empathetic therapist who is now more likely to sit and listen. As a parent, he has taught me patience and resilience and elevated my values of compassion, accountability and service over self.

Call-to-Action Mode

After receiving Kellan's diagnosis of spastic triplegia cerebral palsy, I experienced grief, guilt and fear. I had to face my emotions and, with guidance, develop a skill set to get my mindset ready to help my child. Kellan needed to feel the security of my love and commitment. Eventually, I came to the realization: "I can't just sit and wait. I need to get on with it."

In the beginning, it was downright exhausting. My energy was focused on my nuclear family and keeping the day-to-day routine going. On the home-front, I was often reluctant to ask for help, but later I learned to use these reprieves to refresh my spirit and (somewhat) pace myself. I got my team to-gether and a support system in place.

My support system consisted of Kellan's pediatri-cian, therapist and grandparents. It took time to get this minimal, yet effective, structure in place. It cut down on the endless cycle of one medical provider visit to another. I came to the realization early on that the endless quest of expert medical consult-ations invariably yielded the same recommendations.

Seeking out and finding medical/healthcare providers who have a passion for what they do and do it well has not always been an easy task. There were times I sensed the providers' lack of faith in Kellan's abilities and an unwillingness to extend beyond the rigidity of mainstay clinical practice. Needless to say, when I encountered this resistance, I politely moved on elsewhere as I was able to. My thought process was if the provider was unable to see my child's value or potential, then why are we wasting each other's time. Like any parent, I want what is best for my child. Because I ask questions, it doesn't mean that I am difficult; it means I am involved.

As I mentioned before, this is a long journey. It is wise to surround your child with medical/healthcare providers who set high expectations versus self-limiting expectations on your child's potential. We have received care from some medical professionals who went above and beyond to meet our expectations. I want to acknowledge these providers who are passionate about pediatrics and who see it as their calling.

Anne Knights Rayson

I am so grateful that Anne Knights Rayson was our first physiotherapist. To this day whenever we go to South Africa, we visit Anne and her daughter Lisa, and I keep them up to date on Kellan's shenanigans.

Anne is a neurodevelopmental trained (NDT) physiotherapist in Durban, South Africa. Kellan was referred to her at 1-year old. Anne is kind, compassionate and empathetic to her patients and their families. We saw her religiously two to three times a week. She set the standard high, and as a result, we set our expectations high.

Right from the beginning, she implemented the parent coaching model, empowering the parent to serve their child. As the therapist, she clearly defined and laid out what she expected of me as the mother. She expected me to be physically present at the session to learn as she guided me through Kellan's therapy plan. She educated me on the value of the routine and repetition of the home program to establish movement patterns. Anne provided me with guidance on how to create opportunities for play and how to minimize positions and postures that would put Kellan at risk for joint damage and the inevitable orthopedic surgeries that children with cerebral palsy undergo as they grow.

Even with therapy Kellan's spasticity increased with his attempts at voluntary movement and this led to a vicious cycle. His poor trunk control impacted everything from independent sitting, self-feeding and constipation, to being able to bring his hands together to play with toys. I researched alternative treatment methods. I was told by his doctors to "wait and see." However, my gut told me otherwise, especially as Kellan developed compensatory mechanisms, which, as a physical therapist, I knew in the long term would destroy his joints and muscles. After a year of working with Anne, she mentioned a procedure called selective dorsal rhizotomy (SDR), which I researched to determine if it was a treatment that was in Kellan's best long-term interest.

Dr. T.S. Park and SDR

Selective dorsal rhizotomy (SDR) is an invasive surgical technique that cauterizes selected sensory nerve roots of the spinal cord, using electromyography (EMG) as a guide. Dr. T.S. Park of St. Louis Children's Hospital revolutionized this surgery from a multiple level laminectomy to a single level laminectomy. During a laminectomy, the back of one or more vertebrae is removed to give access to the spinal cord.

To get the care we believed Kellan needed, we moved across the Atlantic Ocean from South Africa to the United States, making our home in Dyersburg, Tennessee, just three hours south of St. Louis, Missouri. I found full-time employment at Physical Therapy of Dyersburg, where I had previously worked as a travel physical therapist.

Kellan's surgery took place on March 12, 2015. Before this surgery, his primary method of mobility was commando crawling, or creeping on his belly. He presented with a Gross Motor Function Classification Scale (GMFCS) 5 at the pre-surgical evaluation. GMFCS is a five-level classification system describing the gross motor function of children with cerebral palsy. It specifically looks at their self-initiated movement while sitting, walking or with wheeled mobility. Levels are classified on a 1 to 5 scale, with 5 being extremely low.

Three months later, Kellan started to crawl up on his hands and knees alternating his arms and legs reciprocally. Six months after the surgery, he started ambulation (walking) with a gait trainer without me propelling him and was able to sit for the first time in a regular chair at a kiddie table.

Karen Pryor, DPT

In 2017, I felt like I was missing something as far as Kellan's mobility. His spasticity ("muscle stiffness" or "tightness") was at least 50 percent reduced, but I could not understand why I was having trouble getting specific muscles to fire in their isolated movement patterns, even with his receiving outpatient therapy and my following through with a home exercise program (HEP) for a one-hour period, five times a week.

As a physical therapist, I received a continuing education flyer about Karen Pryor, DPT, who is based in Nashville, Tennessee, and the work she was doing on neuroplasticity, which is the way the brain can connect and rewire itself to form new pathways for sensory and motor function. I signed up for the course, and from the physical therapy perspective, I learned about the importance of vision, sensory integration and novelty (creating new experiences) in the concept of neuroplasticity.

"We're not always sure what changed the way that our baby moves, talks and functions. What we do know is how to rewire the nervous system in a revolutionary new way with tools for neuroplasticity. Reaching deep into the nervous system areas that go to the fingers and toes and face, as well as neural pathways deep inside the brain stem, midbrain and the cortex, can all be reformatted to increase motor skills and mobility of these young children." — Karen Pryor, DPT

It was a no-brainer that I needed to take Kellan to her for a consultation. We had three sessions over a three-year period. Karen effectively communicated what I needed to do with Kellan after each consultation. She had me video her recommendations. I used these video clips as a reminder of his home program and also as a photo journal to plot his progress. You can listen to Karen discuss "What is

Neuroplasticity?" on Episode 9 of the Raising Kellan
Podcast.

Navigating Life

N avigating life with my child who has cerebral palsy is not a linear pathway nor a "one solution fits all" situation. I have a fundamental understanding that I cannot change or fix Kellan's cerebral palsy. There is no cure, it will follow him for the rest of his life; but there are tools available to help manage the symptoms.

The way Kellan lives and is able to take care of himself is rooted in my actions and proportionate to the effort put into early intervention. How he will move, feed and communicate cannot be guaranteed, but that does not stop me from believing in his potential and working towards his independence.

A team has guided me towards facilitating my child's development. However, as a parent, I research, I ask questions and I question answers to determine what will be in the best longterm interest of my child.

Having said that, be prudent with your sources of information. The internet can sometimes be a two-edged sword of unfiltered information overload; however, it can offer the opportunity to connect and this is the catalyst for www.raisingkellan.org. The intent is to form a digital platform for parents and individuals with developmental delay or a disability to network, learn and collaborate.

Raising Kellan is a lifelong journey with many stumbling blocks along the way, including growth spurts and changes in medical status. But I keep the faith and hold the belief that my child is a survivor who has purpose and is here for a reason.

"As we let our own light shine,
we unconsciously give other people permission
to do the same."
— Nelson Mandela

Life Skills &
Strategies 101

T he luxury of hindsight has evolved into strategies I embrace in our life. I want to share the skills I have utilized in our journey. This is in no way an exhaustive list, nor is it intended as medical advice, it is merely informational and a reflection of what I wish I knew back then.

Acceptance

Acknowledging and accepting Kellan's cerebral palsy was my biggest hurdle as a physical therapist because I knew how the spasticity would destroy his body as he aged and potentially cause him chronic pain. At the time of his diagnosis, receiving the confirmation of what I already knew on a primitive level as a mother allowed me to move forward. This reduced my anxiety, optimized my energy and gave me better mental acuity and focus. Now eight years later, the bells and whistles of the NICU are a distant memory and all I see is my munchkin smiling mischievously at me. Time changes everything, and I am grateful.

Ask for help. I advocate talking to a mental health professional with experience in the area of disability and following up with them as needed. I wish I had met a counselor like Rose Reif early on. She would have put so many of my earlier struggles into perspective. Rose is a licensed clinical mental health counselor, and her private practice, Reif Counseling Services, is located in Cary, North Carolina.

I interviewed Rose on Episode 17 of the Raising Kellan Podcast. I found her to be so in tune with the gamut of challenges an individual with a disability and their caregivers face. Her Mental Wellness + Disability blog is located on her website www.reifpsychservices.com. It is an invaluable resource that contains nuggets of information you will find useful.

Mindset

In my opinion, developing a positive mindset is helpful in preparing yourself for the journey ahead. Your child's journey is not linear: there are many unexpected stops and detours along the way. Like any parent-child dynamic, there is no perfect way to do things. You do your best one day at a time, pacing your mind and body for this journey that is more of a marathon than a sprint.

Your child will reach their milestones in their

time and with your help. This occurs at a different pace for all of us. In the meantime, do not be afraid to create new or modify experiences for your family. Do not let fear or traditional perceptions hold you back from living the life you envision for your family. With time I have learned to give myself permission to dream again and find my joy, celebrating Kellan's big and little accomplishments. I am going to paraphrase Chris Meyer on Episode 16 of the Raising Kellan Podcast where he said: "We love life and life loves us!" **#Truth**

I believe a positive mindset can be learned. I maintain a sense of gratitude to drive me intrinsically and this keeps me motivated to help Kellan work his way towards his independence. Tackling age-appropriate activities, like self-feeding and dressing, for a child with cerebral palsy can be exhausting. It takes patience, routine and repetition day in and day out.

Let's use Kellan learning to brush his teeth as an

example. Sure it's easier for me to do it for him, but that takes away his responsibility for learning that life skill. What happens when I am not there? **#Reality**

To put things into perspective, the one big goal for Kellan in 2019 was for him to learn how to perform his oral care. This activity was broken down into bite-size pieces, or subtasks, and it took 12 months to develop the motor planning, endurance and confidence to brush his teeth by himself. We celebrated this big, little accomplishment, and it fuels us for the next mission.

Accountability of the Home Exercise Program

Kellan received his therapy before age 5 in a traditional outpatient setting. This experience was valuable in teaching me the skills of how to handle his body. Now that Kellan is older, we focus on his tailored home exercise program.

For the last few years, we have checked back with the therapists at St. Louis Children's Hospital for bi-annual therapy intensives for home program updates. Going for these weeklong therapy intensives every six months keeps us accountable on an extrinsic level. This arrangement is working well for us at present and gives us more flexibility with afternoons during the school year. With the caveat that we have taken ownership of his mobility training, afternoons are no longer spent racing from one therapy appointment to another. We do the home program through the week, splitting it into 30-minute sessions in the morning and afternoon.

I believe the consistency of doing some kind of exercise program is a valuable concept for Kellan to grasp and comprehend. I hope to nurture the importance of exercise and for him to develop this accountability as he gets older. This tool will help him manage his cerebral palsy as he grows into his ever-changing body — decoding and unlocking his potential as he zooms towards adulthood. Novelty and creating new opportunities for him to learn how to use and move his body have definitely kept things fresh and motivating for him.

Think Outside the Box

Kellan does not participate in traditional sports; however, we have discovered other avenues for him to enjoy the outdoors and participate in social events.

Tri-My-Best Adaptive Triathlon is a yearly event held in various United States cities including St. Louis, Missouri; Augusta, Georgia; New Orleans, Louisiana; and Nashville, Tennessee. It is a swim/bike/run race to encourage children of ALL abilities to participate with their adaptive equipment as needed. Children are teamed up with a "buddy" for teamwork and support.

In my opinion, this event gives Kellan an opportunity to compete with his peers while building independence, self-esteem and confidence. We typically participate in the Nashville race sponsored by Monroe Carell Jr. Children's Hospital at Vanderbilt. Last year, we were unable to go to Nashville, and Kellan was disappointed. Thankfully, we found out about the St. Louis race, and he was able to compete in his "sports day."

The home exercise program is a challenging routine. The Tri-My-Best Adaptive Triathlon is why we continue to bust it day in and day out. Once a year, Kellan gets to see the benefit of exercising and maintaining his physical fitness. My guy should be motivated to rock out his home exercises for the coming year until the next triathlon, and I have an objective measure of how he is physically progressing.

The weekends are free for Kellan to enjoy his extracurricular activity, which is therapeutic horsemanship. We are extremely fortunate to have a therapeutic riding center right here in Dyersburg. **Healing Horses, Inc.** is a nonprofit organization founded by Sonya Burks and is a **PATH (Professional Association of Therapeutic Horsemanship)** certified center.

Therapeutic horsemanship allows individuals with disabilities to harness the healing power of the human-horse connection. In Kellan's case, the three-dimensional rotation of the horse models human gait. This sensory feedback helps his trunk develop postural control, balance and strength as he unknowingly adjusts his core to keep in sync with Dakota, a sweet-tempered American Paint Horse. **This is therapy at it's best — therapy that is fun**; t**herapy that has you working without you even knowing it.**

Yes, horse riding has improved Kellan's **mobility,** but it also helped with his **lung volume control and speech production**. It gives him a sense of **confidence**. It gets him outdoors and wires him for a different experience outside the neurotypical, school and home environments.

Support Systems

I cloak myself with a support system that uplifts me. The power of faith is something I can testify to. I am grateful for the friends who stand by and support us in times of need.

Our example of "it takes a village" is when Kellan and I moved to Dyersburg in October 2014. The childcare I set up fell through the weekend before I was scheduled to start my full-time job. A dear friend of mine, Lindsay Viser, helped me contact Beth LeMay, a retired nurse, who took care of Kellan while I worked.

Later on, Tammy Yates cared for Kellan and was there for us as Kellan went through his surgery and started school. Previously a paraprofessional,

Tammy was a teacher's assistant to a student with cerebral palsy, so she had a multi-layered knowledge base, including her most important credential — she is mom to Thomas, a gentle, artistic young adult with autism. I believe our families were a mutual source of encouragement to each other.

I will be forever grateful for the love and kindness bestowed on us by our Dyersburg family and the two community groups we participate in. God's Hands is a group of young adults from the First United Methodist Church that meets on Wednesday nights to fellowship and participate in community events. B.U.D.S (Being United and Developing Support) is an informal playgroup for kids of all abilities founded by Amy Day, who is the mother of a special needs child.

How Amy and I initially met is another example of it takes a village. For up to a year after Kellan's surgery, we lived in a tiny apartment. It was difficult for him to negotiate around our space with his bulky gait trainer to practice the walking needed to strengthen his muscles. When I got home in the evenings, Kellan and I would head to a local retail pharmacy to buy a few odds and ends. This 10,000-square-foot building provided plenty of room for Kellan to log his walking. It was a nontraditional place for him to exercise while sheltering from the sweltering southern summers and chilly winter nights.

The main incentive was to get out of the apartment, where he spent most of his day with his caregiver. It was a place for him to be out and about in the community. Amy was the assistant manager at the time and, together with Marie and Meagan Littlejohn and Ethan Seratt, provided friendship and support. Kellan started with taking 10 minutes to get from the front door to the first aisle, but with time and coaxing from this fantastic team of coworkers, Kellan was soon able to trek from one end of the store to the other. Amy, Marie, Ethan, Gloria and other staff members became his cheerleaders, an unlikely but much appreciated and valued support system.

Technology keeps us connected to our family who live far away. Grandparents hold a special place in any child's heart, and Kellan's morning does not get going until he video calls "his people." He loves to chat with his grandparents, finding out about their day and telling them about his "stories."

We love to travel. Last year we visited our family in South Africa and got to take part in the unique experience of going on a safari. We also caught up with our beloved Anne Knights Rayson, Kellan's first physiotherapist.

"And now these three remain: faith, hope and love. But the greatest of these is love."
— 1 Corinthians 13:13

Self-Advocacy

There is an inherent human curiosity towards anyone who does not fit the status quo. I try to be transparent regarding Kellan's cerebral palsy.

I must admit, questions regarding "What's wrong with him?" used to tick me off, but with experience comes wisdom and, generally speaking, a thicker skin. Personally, I choose to educate and create awareness with the caveat that I tend to use the least amount of words to get the point across. When asked, "Will he grow out of it?" My answer simply is, "No."

I have schooled Kellan when reference is made to his cerebral palsy to hold his head up and speak his truth. Here again, I am grateful for his ability to self-advocate.

> *"Never bend your head.*
> *Always hold it high.*

Look the world straight in the eye."

—Helen Keller

Motivation

There are times when I get into a funk, especially when change is slow to come and during growth spurts when we experience crushing setbacks. During this time, we have to work 10 times harder to not lose gains made. Sometimes, we have to re-learn skills once mastered. But rest assured, we keep practicing and eventually change does come. We embrace the opportunity to learn together on this difficult, but not impossible, journey.

I will be the first to admit, staying motivated is not always easy when you carry a full load — trying to balance your home and work lives. When I need encouragement, I often go to two resources.

The first is the book *Ten fingers, Ten Toes Twenty*

Things Everyone Needs to Know: Neuroplasticity for Children by Karen Pryor, Ph.D., PT, DPT. Her work is based on neuroplasticity and the ability of the brain to "rewire" using multisensory and novel activities to create new neural pathways and affect changes in functional movement. I will never forget her question, which still resonates with me today: "Do you want to work hard now or for the rest of your life?" This honesty, I must admit, often fuels me when I feel like I have nothing left to give.

The second is Dr. Karen Pape's book *The Boy Who Could Run But Not Walk: Understanding Neuroplasticity in the Child's Brain.* The late Dr. Pape was a neonatologist and a clinical neuroscientist from Toronto, Canada. During her clinical practice, she observed what she termed as "outliers." This term described low birth weight, preterm infants who had developed various types of brain damage, as documented on brain scans in NICU, and who had made an unexpected and complete recovery. This phenomenon was linked to neuroplasticity and the ability of the brain to recover and heal. She described the concept of how habit can hide recovery and gives the example of her patient, and hence the title of the book. My takeaway from her was the age-old adage of "use it or lose it."

Conclusion

I often end the Raising Kellan Podcast with my mantra: "Always get to the top of your mountain."

This has become my driver. It is entrenched in my mindset with a singularity that cultivates focus amidst chaos.

Raising my son Kellan is difficult but not impossible. However, when I reflect back to those early years, I often wonder how different things would have been if I could have connected with parents on a similar journey.

I encourage you to connect with other parents and find the driver that motivates you to keep on going to help your child. Breaking long-term goals into bite-size goals allows you to scale what may seem like an insurmountable mountain. As cliche as it may sound, always remember that you are not alone.

Summary

I n brief, this is what I wish I knew back then:

- Pace and prepare my mindset for the long haul and view my journey as a marathon versus a sprint.

- Understand the understated importance of beginning an early intervention program as soon as possible and provide varied multi-sensory experiences for my child to learn and grow.

- Develop intrinsic motivation and focus as a parent to do the work now for the carryover needed to unlock my child's potential.

- Surround myself with two things: medical

professionals who are willing to coach and advise me as a partner in my child's development and a network of family, friends and community to support me as I need.

The Present

It is May 2020, and we are amid the coronavirus pandemic. We were travelling to St. Louis Children's Hospital on March 16, 2020, for an intensive weeklong therapy session and a follow up with Dr. Park when news of the pandemic started gaining media attention in the United States. It was almost eerie driving the interstate from Dyersburg, Tennessee, to St. Louis, Missouri, where the streets were devoid of their usual bumper-to-bumper traffic.

All sporting events were canceled on March 15, but things quickly evolved with school closures, restaurants offering curbside-service only, and on Friday, March 20, elective surgeries at the hospital were canceled. We were the last patients seen that Friday as the hospital's outpatient therapy department was closed until further notice. We hurried back to Tennessee that afternoon as Governor Bill Lee issued a Shelter-in-Place Order.

It is indeed a strange and uncertain time. Time will reveal how COVID-19 impacts the way we live in our communities and how we adapt to these changes.

At present, I am homeschooling Kellan with the school closures. He will transition to third grade at Dyersburg Intermediate School when school gets back into session. Our goal is for Kellan to be mainstreamed, but for now, we value the benefit of the special needs classroom as he builds on his foundational skills. He also receives weekly PT/OT/SPT services at school. At present, Kellan is a GMFCS 3 and is working towards crutch walking.

Epilogue

I initiated Raising Kellan, Inc. as a self-funded project in June 2019 after we traveled to South Africa to visit family. I am grateful to the therapists at Open Air School in Durban for giving me an opportunity to create awareness by presenting at a continuing education seminar on June 6, 2019.

I talked about selective dorsal rhizotomy, neuroplasticity and empowering the parent to keep their child motivated and moving. The feedback I received after that presentation became the seed for my mission to educate and empower parents raising children with different abilities.

After coming back to the States, I did some self-reflection. I wanted to pass on my experiences of raising my child with cerebral palsy and the strategies I believe help us. I wanted to create a platform of shared experiences so ordinary parents faced with extraordinary challenges know they are not alone. I wanted parents to know there are others doing the daily grind who are not sure of the exact outcomes, but also are not willing to sit back and "wait and see."

The last year has been an incredible journey. It started with a seed, an idea to create a community. I wanted to make sure the content and shared information had a digital platform that could be accessed anytime, anywhere by any parent looking for it. The Raising Kellan Blog was born in June 2019 with the technical help of Dennis Anderson and later Steve Herren.

In October 2019, the blog evolved into a podcast. This was inspired by Drake Box, a young man with cerebral palsy who has now gone on to produce his own podcast, The Box Factor. You can hear more about the origin story of the podcast, as well as Drake's journey, on Episode 1 of the Raising Kellan Podcast, which can be accessed through Apple, Google and Spotify. Special thanks to Alan Ingalls and Matthew Sims for their technical podcasting skills.

The Raising Kellan Blog and Podcast are hosted on the website www.raisingkellan.org. Both platforms contain relevant content that provides value to parents and individuals in our community. If you would like to contribute content or share your story, you can reach me at raisingkellan@gmail.com.

I am incredibly grateful for the amazing friendships that have developed from this digital community.

An example of such a friendship is Drake Box, a young adult with cerebral palsy, I interviewed on Episode 1 of the Raising Kellan Podcast. Drake was adopted at two-years-old from Ukraine by Gary and Laurie Box of Dyersburg, Tennessee. I met him at a local grocery store where is worked as a clerk. We struck up a conversation related to why Kellan used a walker. The moment he stated that he had cerebral palsy will be one that is etched in my mind forever. At that instant I did not trust myself to speak or ask questions I was curious about. Three days later, in the outpatient therapy clinic I worked at, I was asked to have a student shadow me so they could accure the hours needed to apply to the physical therapy assistant program. Low and behold, as I opened the curtain of the patient treatment cubicle, that young man from the grocery store stood there before me. Since then, Drake has unofficially become part of our family and the motivation for initiating the podcast.

Christine Coronado and her family opened a mom-and-pop convenience store in Dyersburg, Tennessee, called **Jordan's Grab and Go.** My appreciation for Jordan's is based on its unique menu, as well as the inspiration for its creation. Jordan is an autistic young adult. Her mother Christine wanted to create a social and work opportunity for Jordan and others with disabilities in our community. You can hear about this amazing venture on Episode 3 of the Raising Kellan Podcast.

Jae Puente co-hosts the **Let's Discuss It** podcast with his brother Ant Puente. This podcast creates a platform for open discussions on relevant topics. Listen to Jae's perspective of raising his son Noah, a child with complex medical needs, on Episode 5 of the Raising Kellan Podcast.

Mindy Silva is a pediatric physical therapist and tech guru living in New Zealand. She is the founder of **wiredONdevelopment**. This Facebook group provides a valuable resource in the niche of neuro-motor rehabilitation and childhood disability. She shared her story on Episode 6 of the Raising Kellan Podcast.

Jessica Leving created the Special Siblings Podcast and book as a resource for neurotypical siblings based on her experience of growing up with Billy, her autistic younger brother. You can hear more about this resource on Episode 7.

In Episode 8 of Love those Books! Kathryn McBride, Director of the McIvers Grant Public Library, gives nuggets of advice on how to nuture the love of reading for our little ones. She provides insight into the question: "Whose responsibility is Early Literacy?"

Chris Meyer, from Seigbury, Germany, co-parents Jade, his 7-year-old daughter with cerebral palsy. Chris describes himself as "a Dad with Passion." Throughout Germany, he often teams up with Jade to host motivational seminars teaching a positive mindset. You will appreciate his straight talk on Episode 16 of The Raising Kellan Podcast.

During April to May 2020, we did a Quarantine Strategy Series during the Covid 19 pandemic.

In Part 1 /Episode 17 with Rose Reif, we discussed Mental Health Strategies.

Part 2/Episode 18, focused on exercise, yoga and relaxation. Here I chat with Maddison Balk, OT and founder of Let's Yoga Perth. Her focus is on improving a child's emotional regulation, motor development and social skills. This well-being is achieved by breath awareness and mindfulness strategies, and connecting with others through games and partner work. She coaches parents and children on strategies they can apply in the community and school to feel calm, accepted, emotionally and sensory regulated, and confident to develop and sustain friendships.

In Part 3/Episode 19 of the Quarantine Series I interviewed Misha Davydov. Here we disccussed the restorative power of nature. Misha is an early childhood educator at A New Leaf Preschool in Nashville,Tennessee. This nature school/farm is inspired by the Reggio Emilia Philosphy where a child is encouraged to learn from the environment. Misha's passion for teaching is evident in his blog journal www.withoutwindows.com

Nicole Luongo is an author, disability advocate and writer. In 2019, Nicole became the first person to get at least one building or landmark in almost all 50 of the United States and three international countries to light up in green on National Cerebral Palsy Awareness Day (annually observed on March 25) and on World Cerebral Palsy Day (annually observed on October 6). You can hear more about this remarkable achievement when I chat with Nicole on Episode 20 of the Raising Kellan Podcast.

Wesley Page, OTR/L, has the unique perspective of being an occupational therapist with cerebral palsy. He graduated from the University of Tennessee at Chattanooga and is a full-time pediatric therapist at the Shrine School in Memphis, Tennessee. You can listen to him on Episode 21 of the Raising Kellan Podcast.

In Episode 22, Hannah Webster, DPT chats about her role as graduate research assistant to Dr Jennifer Tucker, DPT, PCS in the Go Baby Go! Program at the Univeristy of Central Florida. This is a national program providing accessible adaptive solutions for children and adults with mobility impairment. The founder of the Go Baby Go! is Cole Galloway from the University of Delaware. He desires to enigneer everyday items to restore the physical independence of self-directed mobility, such as adapting ride-on cars with things like PVC pipe and foam.

In Episode 23, Todd Williams, DPT talks about his experiece of preparing and running the New York City Marathon in 2019. Todd ran to advocate and create awareness for cerebral palsy as well as Achilles International, an organization whose mission is to empower peolple of all disabilities to participate in mainstream running events. Todd blogs at www.ptwithcp.com, where he also tells mobility stories of other young adults.

In Episode 24, Genesis Emery is an entreprenuer, speaker, and philanthropist. She is a single mom and a special needs parent to Noah, her 5-year-old son with Rubinstein Taybi Syndrome. Noah is the inspiration for her business, The Little Dapper Collection, which sells handcrafted bow ties with a mission to groom little boys into dapper young gentleman. Genesis has humbly turned her economic empowerment into social responsibility by creating The Little Dapper Project, a nonprofit in her hometown of Chicago, Illinois that provides a program for at risk youth. #Mamas Making Money Mondays is her online IGTV show that teaches moms about being an entrepreneur.

Dana Kramer (Episode 12), Lauren Taylor (Episode 15) and Aspen Balthazor (Episode 10) are amazing and talented moms. They have graciously agreed to be contributing authors to this book and share their perspectives of raising their children with different abilities in the next few pages.

Accepting The Weight
Of The Crown
By Dana Kramer

T he day I've tried so hard to forget has become the day I will always remember. The day the doctor so casually uttered the words, as if he were reading them from a script. The day I learned the life I had always imagined for my child would never come to fruition. Little did I know then that God had much bigger plans for us and I would quickly learn normal is highly overrated.

Levi, my precious miracle baby, was diagnosed with cerebral palsy on that day and was predicted to never walk, talk or eat on his own. He was 13-months old.

Time stood still. I felt I had been lifted out of my body and was watching this happen to someone else. After receiving such life-shattering news, we were quickly shuffled out of the patient room and told to return for an MRI confirmation at age 2. Levi's father and I found ourselves motionless in the parking lot with nothing left to do but cry.

I often think how different it would've been if I knew then what I know now. If only I knew then that my son's future would be nothing like what the doctor predicted on that infamously unforgettable day. If only I could tell my former self that it's okay to grieve but don't be in denial, don't try to fix it — try to embrace the challenge. As soon as the initial shock and grief pass, you have to straighten up your momma crown high on your head because life will be hard for you and your son, but we will never cease to fight that much harder.

If only I knew back then, seven years ago, that he would refuse to allow this diagnosis to hold him back. Developmentally disabled little boy? Not Levi. He will become a beast!

He will be happy, brave and determined to beat the odds stacked against him. Not only will he conquer walking, talking and eating on his own, he will play sports, have friends, excel in school and, at 8-years old, even manage his own Instagram account, @levis_cp_life, which he created to share his story and inspire the world.

The person you were before this journey will begin to fade with each new day. You will become a new woman with an advanced perspective and an appreciation for the little things in life you never knew you were missing.

Sure, this wasn't the journey you intended to take, but you will learn to be grateful that it was the journey you were given. Once you accept this new you, while clinging tight to your faith in God, you will find there is light at the end of the tunnel much closer than you think. When the world seems cold, clasp on to Jesus and let your soul take control. After all, He only gives the toughest battles to His strongest warriors.

Dana Kramer
Georgia, USA

Nevada Brew Works

By Lauren Taylor

N evada Brew Works is a family-owned brewery located in Las Vegas that was inspired by a 1-pound, 14-ounce miracle baby.

The story begins in 2016 when Lauren became pregnant with Ariana Rye. Her pregnancy had difficulties throughout, including symptoms like swelling and joint pain. On January 30, 2017, Lauren got home from work and began to hemorrhage. Jason, Lauren's husband, drove her to the hospital. Ariana was born that night, 3.5 months early at 26+0 weeks. Lauren's official diagnosis was placental abruption caused by severe pre-eclampsia.

Lauren and Jason were told the hospital would do everything they could to save Ariana's life. Ariana was sent immediately to the NICU where she spent the next 117 days. Due to her extreme prematurity, doctors didn't know what long-term prognosis Ariana might face. After a year of achieving no motor milestones, Ariana Rye was diagnosed with spastic quadriplegic cerebral palsy.

The diagnosis didn't scare the couple then, and it still doesn't. In their view, the diagnosis doesn't change who Ariana is or how much they love her. Now they face the daunting challenge of obtaining the care, treatment and equipment necessary to suit her special needs.

Jason and Lauren have always been craft beer lovers. As Ariana turned 2-years old, the couple continued to face the hardship of taking Ariana to multiple medical appointments and fighting with insurance for medical equipment. They knew the time was right to begin work on their new business venture to give Ariana a brighter future. Lauren's father, Ken, was enlisted as the brewmaster and Nevada Brew Works was born.

Ariana Rye was the catalyst they needed to get the business started. She is why they are brewing for a cause. The word "Brew" in their logo is green, which stands for cerebral palsy. They will have a beer named after Ariana Rye, known as the Ariana Rye PA. Proceeds from the beer will be donated to local organizations such as NICUs, Little Miss Hannah Foundation, Opportunity Village and more. They will also have a monthly rotating beer on tap named after a different medically complex child to raise money to buy equipment for that sponsored child. The inspiration for the rotating tap was from another micro-preemie child named Oliver.

When people come to Nevada Brew Works, they will be drinking for a cause and raising money for kids like Ariana. Nevada Brew Works also wants to share the stories of other medically complex kids while raising awareness for different medical conditions.

The kid-friendly brewery is slated to open in the summer of 2020 in Las Vegas. Ariana Rye, now 3, will be employed as the assistant to the brewmaster. She won't be calling the brewmaster "boss" though; she refers to him as "Papa."

Lauren Taylor

Las Vegas, Nevada

'Get Up And Get Moving'

By Aspen Balthazor

from the Raising Kellan Blog

My name is Aspen Balthazor. I am a doctor of physical therapy in Wichita, Kansas. I specialize in working with people with neurological diseases/disorders, as well as the geriatric population to age in place safely. I have 9-year-old twins Tenley and Camden. I am honored to share our journey with our unique situation of my daughter Tenley having cerebral palsy and my now being her full-time physical therapist.

Tenley and her twin brother Camden entered this world 11 weeks early to save all three of our lives.

On November 1, 2010, the ultrasound tech was taking much longer than usual to get the images my obstetrician-gynecologist Dr. Zachary Kuhlmann requested daily. Within minutes of returning to my hospital room and climbing into bed, a nurse entered stating: "We are headed to labor and delivery." Within the hour of arriving at labor and delivery, Dr. Kuhlmann entered the room stating: "Today is going to be Tenley and Camden's birthday. We have 24 hours to get Camden out and keep all three of you safe." He informed us the umbilical cord flow had changed direction from Camden and was flowing back to me.

Camden had a rough eight weeks in the NICU following their delivery at 29 weeks. Tenley, on the other hand, sailed through her six-week NICU stay, being labeled by neonatal medicine specialist Dr. Curtis Dorn as the "NICU MVP." Dr. Dorn said, "If Tenley had a jersey, we would hang it on the wall."

*"For I know the plans I have for you declares
the Lord, plans to prosper you and not harm*

you, plans to give you hope and a future."
—Jeremiah 29:11

As Tenley approached 8-months old, we noticed she was not reaching her milestones. At that time, we were told by her pediatrician not to compare Tenley to Camden at this age, and he informed us she was fine. I, however, knew her body felt different and could see the struggles she was facing daily trying to keep up with Camden. Fast forward to September 30, 2014: we received MRI confirmation of damage in Tenley's brain leading to the diagnosis of spastic diplegia cerebral palsy.

Tenley has undergone the following treatments to date: physical therapy for seven years; two trials of oral baclofen; hippotherapy for three years; Botox injections in September 2014; selective dorsal rhizotomy by Dr. T.S. Park in February 2015; PERCS (lengthening) for gastrocnemius release in December 2015; and anterior tibialis tendon transfer with Achilles PERCS in May 2018 by Dr. Matthew

Dobbs.

Therapy has been amazing for Tenley. In our opinion, Tenley has had the best therapists and we have a supportive, amazing family. Without everyone's joint efforts, Tenley would not be as independent as she is. Tenley's early years of physical therapy proved to be challenging with my being a physical therapist. I was constantly assessing and correcting her movement patterns, and this began to build a wedge between us. Tenley did not always like for me to be present during her treatment sessions and would take out her frustrations on me. I have been hit in the face, spat on and bitten by what the rest of the world knows as our sweet Tenley. Tenley's therapist at the time recommended I stay in the waiting room for sessions. This was the moment I began to realize that during this phase of our lives, I needed to be "Mom" as much as possible and not her physical therapist.

As Tenley grew older, we faced surgeries to improve her mobility, pain and alignment. We faced these procedures and hospital stays as a family. I would stay in the hospital room with her overnight; Daddy would come in the morning to take over and allow me some rest. My parents often traveled with us for support, and my in-laws held down the fort back home caring for Camden. During this time, things began to change: Tenley began to trust in me as a mom and a physical therapist.

My first advice from our journey is to have friends or family available to help and not be afraid to ask for help. If you do not have family or friends nearby, then search for local support groups or ask your doctors and therapists for guidance to find some. My mother has been a lifeline for me since I became pregnant: always answering my phone calls listening to my fears, tears and joys, and always having the ability to make it better. The best advice my mother has given me along the way was: "Aspen, you are going to have to quit feeling sorry for your-self and Tenley. Sitting here crying for hours is not going to change anything. It is okay for a little bit, but then you need to get up and get moving for Ten-ley and your family."

My mother was oh so right! Little did I know at that time that I appeared to be fine and function-ing, but I was slowly falling into a deep depres-sion. People on the outside looking in had no idea. My close friends probably had ideas as I confided in them at times, but honestly looking back on it now, I am not sure they realized how bad it was. I am not sure I realized how bad it was until I now reflect on it. I functioned because I did not have any other choice. My husband is a police officer and his sched-ule is never predictable. I was the only constant for our family. On top of all of it, I was a physical therapist with the mindset that I should be able to "fix" Tenley. This spiraled me into dark places that progressed for several years. All during this time, I finally became Tenley's main physical therapist and she began enjoying "working out with Mommy," seeing my love and dedication to help her versus just correcting her. We made the workouts fun, never the same, and we found the best flow was for me to pick an exercise then Tenley would choose one. This allowed Tenley to feel she had an active role in her treatment, and this has worked well for us.

We have traveled to California and Texas for months at a time to have Tenley participate in intensive therapy sessions lasting two to three hours per day. We transformed our basement storage room into our gym space. We had fundraisers to help fund trips for therapy as well as fund items needed for her home gym. During this time, I realized I needed professional help for the depression and anxiety I was facing. It was beginning to take a toll on our family. I cannot begin to describe the blessing my therapist and doctors have been over the last few years.

So, the next advice I have is to seek professional help for yourself when you need it. It really is true that if you do no take care of yourself, you will not be able to care for anyone else.

> *"My grace is sufficient for you, for my power is made perfect in weakness. Therefore, I will boast all the more gladly about my weaknesses, so that Christ's power may rest on me. That is why, for Christ's sake I delight in weakness, in insults, in hardships, in persecutions, in difficulties. For when I am weak, then I am strong."*
> — 2 Corinthians 12:9

Tenley is now 9-years old and continues to love the phrase she has been saying since she was 2: "I will do it myself!" The drive for independence this girl has is phenomenal. We have our weeks where we are very consistent with therapy at home, then we go weeks without being consistent. Our best way to stay motivated is a dry erase calendar hanging on our gym wall. Tenley makes a checkmark and notes her duration exercised after each session. Tenley then makes a goal for the end of the week she wants to achieve. I love seeing her face when she knocks out that goal! I no longer stress over missed workouts. Several years ago, this used to eat me alive. However, I have finally accepted the fact that I will never "fix" her movement patterns. We can improve strength, balance and movement patterns giving her the best quality of independent life. But I am not willing to sacrifice our relationship or her years of just being a carefree little girl at the expense of making sure we include one more workout.

My last bit of advice is to find balance. Find what your child has a passion for and allow that to shine. Know it is okay to let that take the place of a workout or two and do not beat yourself up about it. Tenley's passion is horses and she attends riding lessons one to two times a week. This past fall, she participated in her first-ever rodeo season and brought home some ribbons! Horse riding lessons and rodeos take away from time we could be focused on workouts at home; however, the joy we see on her face watching her accomplish the goals she sets in her passion is worth it!

Consider it pure joy, my brothers and sisters, whenever you face trials of many kinds, because you know that the testing of your faith produces perseverance. Let perseverance finish its work so that you may be mature and complete, not lacking anything.
—James 1:2-4

Aspen Balthazor, DPT
Wichita, Kansas

Acknowledgments

Raising Kellan has taken a village.

· Through our journey I have no doubt that we have been guided by God's hand.

*"Faith is the reality of what we hope for,
the proof of what we don't see."*

— Hebrews 11:1

· Our parents Dr. P.K. Naidoo, Mano Naidoo, Dhaya Jagernath and family.

· Our educators in the Dyersburg City Schools.

· Our medical providers Dr. Stevens D. Melton and Dr. T.S. Park.

· Our local therapists Ms. Kelley McBride, Ms. Valerie, Ms. Emilee; Ms. Amy, Ms. Shelley and Ms. Jo Beth; along with therapists at St. Louis Children's Hospital, Deanna Walters, Jackie Patterson, Becca Oschwald, Tori Courts, Bailey Hargis and Caroline

Thompson.

• Our friends: Ruth Bowlin of Memphis; Mary Frances Anthony; John and Mary Alice Higdon; Tammy, Paul and Thomas Yates; Tracy Rendon; Anna Cutler; Lindsay Viser; Beth LeMay; Elenor Nunn; Norma Roberts; Judy Naidoo; Shanaaz Khan; Sonya and B.J. Burks; Patti Lou and Betsy Parker; Marie Littlejohn; Dennis Anderson; Ed Presley; Miranda Jackson; Shelby Fisk; Jeremy Lee; Matthew Simms; Alan Ingalls; Lavanya Wiles; Kerchia Naidoo; Dr. Karen Bowyer; Vanessa Romer Cain; Hannah Webster,DPT; Jackie Butch,SPT; Marianna Wright,DPT; Lucy Chetty,OT; Rene Naidoo,PT; Beattie Lombard; Will Clark; and Namira Haripersad.

• The volunteer board of Raising Kellan, Inc.: Steve Herren, Judy Hatch, Zaira Martin and Hope Khalil.

• Our church family at First United Methodist Church in Dyersburg, Tennessee.

About The Author

Marsh Naidoo lives in Dyersburg, Tennessee, with her husband Prakash and 8-year-old son Kellan. They enjoy being out in the community, traveling and therapeutic horse riding at a local nonprofit called Healing Horses, Inc.

Marsh blogs at www.raisingkellan.org and produces the Raising Kellan Podcast. Both mediums provide relevant content to the community of parents raising children with special needs.

BOOK REVIEWS

Marsh Naidoo's book serves to educate and inspire parents who have recently learned that their child has a disability. The author explains that early intervention (EI) is crucial to a child's long term success. This book provides a friendly and encouraging voice to parents who may feel alone on their journey. Marsh and other mothers openly and honestly share the challenges, fears and adventures they have encountered as they strive to help their children be all they can be. You will find this book to be a helpful tool to lead you "to the top of your mountain."

—Angela Brasher, Speech-Language Pathologist, Memphis, United States of America

I found this book to be captivating, informative and inspiring. Once I started, I couldn't put it down. I loved the positive approach of the author and how she encourages her child "to hold his head up and speak his truth." I am sure that this will be helpful to others in their journey.

—Deborah Keenan, Dyersburg, United States of America

Marsh's journey will resonate with many parents of a special needs child. But what makes this read different is that it is also a thought-provoking and practical philosphy that will help any parent navigate the murky web of medical and therapeutic interventions whilst maintaining mental wellbeing. The "what I wish I knew back then" insights are simply invaluable coming from a fellow parent.

—Namira Haripersad, Parent, South Africa

This is a MUST READ!!! With this book you can feel Marsh's sincerity in expressing the different emotions she experiences as a mother raising Kellan. You can grasp her optimism that Kellan will be in a better place through hard work and advocacy for him to reach his full potential. The words that she used in writing this book are simple yet POWERFUL. Marsh's openness in dealing with the realities of Kellan's special needs-the challenges and the disappointments along the way, the countless hours spent on his home program, medical appointments , and expanding her support system through church, friends, organizations and family-gives inspiration to other special needs parents that this journey can be done with grace, faith, strength and perseverance. Even though she is a physical therapist she knows that her primary role is being a MOTHER to love, support ,and raise Kellan to be the best that he can be in life.

—Eugene Gonzales, PT, Memphis, United States of America

I just want to say thank you, thank you for writing this! I could have written it myself. It is full of the highs and lows of this journey we all share and it made me cry and gave me hope that some people do understand this journey. I see so many "obedient" and non "dfficult" parents at all of our appointments and I admit - sometimes I start to wonder if I'm going crazy! So THANK YOU!

—Monique Webber, Parent, Australia

W hat a wonderful and honest book written for the benefit of both parents and PTs alike! I would recommend this book to new grads looking into pediatrics, seasoned PTs, and parents that are just starting their journey after their little one is diagnosed with developmental delay. There truly is something in it for everyone. I can't wait to see this book hit the shelves!

—Coryann Ledford, DPT, California, United States of America

PODCASTS

Episode 1: My First 19 Years Living with Cerebral Palsy.

Episode 2: What parents need to know when language and speech development is delayed.

Episode 3: Parents open fast food restaurant to give daughter with Autism purpose.

Episode 4: Is Horse Riding an effective therapy tool?

Episode 5: Podcasters & Parents of Kids with cerebral palsy.

Episode 6: Wired on Development, an internet based
        knowledge hub.

Episode 7: Supporting Special Needs Siblings.

Epiode 8: Love those Books!

Episode 9: What is Neuroplasticity?

Episode 10: Aspen Joy Balthazor, DPT

Episode 11: American Physical Therapy Conference CSM 2020

Episode 12: Cerebral Plasy Awareness Month

Episode 13: A Travel Blog on Embracing the Unexpected and   Facing the Unknown.

Episode 14: Honoring our CP Warriors.

Episode 15: Nevada Brew Works.

Episode 16: Chris Meyer and his Positive Mindset Strategies.

Episode 17: Quarantine Series, Part 1 on Mental Health.

Episode 18: Quarantine Series, Part 2 on Exercise,Yoga and Relaxation.

Episode 19: Quaratine Series, Part 3 on the Restorative Power of Nature.

Episode 20: Nicole Luongo: Author, Poet and Disability Advocate.

Episode 21: Wesley Page, OT. The Perspective of an Occupational Therapist with Cerebral Palsy.

Episode 22: Go Baby Go!

Podcasts are avaliable on your podcast provider including Apple, Anchor, Google and Spotify.

ILLUSTRATIONS

by

Hope Khalil

Hope Khalil was born in Chicago,Illinois and began drawing at the early age of three. She has been in the educational field for 24 years and is a self-taught artist now living in Friendship,Tennessee.

New Beginnings (pg4)

This is not the End.
It's just the beginning...

Made in the USA
Middletown, DE
19 August 2020